THE GREAT MARRIAGE EXPERIENCE VIDEO SERIES

THE 5 SEX NEEDS

OF MEN AND WOMEN

DR. GARY AND BARBARA ROSBERG

LifeWay Press
Nashville, Tennessee

Published by LifeWay Press®
© 2007 Gary and Barb Rosberg

ISBN 978-1-14158-6392-3
Item 005112688

This book is course CG-1317 in the Personal Life
category of the Christian Growth Study Plan.

Dewey Decimal Classification: 155.3
Subject Headings: SEXUAL BEHAVIOR \ MARRIAGE \ MARRIED PEOPLE—SEXUAL

To order additional copies of this resource, write LifeWay Church Resources
Customer Service; One LifeWay Plaza; Nashville, TN 37234-0013;
FAX (615) 251-5933; call toll-free (800) 458-2772; order online at *www.lifeway.com;*
e-mail *orderentry@lifeway.com;* or visit the LifeWay Christian Store serving you.

Printed in the United States of America

Leadership and Adult Publishing
LifeWay Church Resources
One LifeWay Plaza
Nashville, TN 37234-0175

DEDICATION

Thank you to Bill Craig who gave us the vision for this video series to strengthen the marriages of America and beyond.

Thank you Brian Czock and his team at SonLight Productions and Bill Dallas and his team at Church Communication Network for bringing this material to life on video. Thank you to the LifeWay publishing family and to Ron Beers for publishing the book bringing this material to the reader.

And mostly, thank you to Jesus Christ for giving us life and the passion to speak boldly about great sex in a godly marriage!

CONTENTS

Dr. Gary and Barb Rosberg host a popular nationally syndicated radio program called "Dr. Gary and Barb Rosberg—Your Marriage Coaches." Award-winning authors and marriage conference speakers, the Rosbergs have written over a dozen prominent marriage and family resources including *6 Secrets to a Lasting Love, 40 Unforgettable Dates with Your Mate,* and the trade book, *The 5 Sex Needs of Men and Women.*

Gary, who earned his Ed.D. from Drake University, has been a marriage and family counselor for more than 25 years. Barb earned her BFA from Drake University and is a sought-after speaker for women's groups and other ministries.

For more information on the Rosbergs' ministry, call (888) 608-COACH or visit *www.drgaryandbarb.com.*

Susan Lanford wrote the viewer guide. Susan is Director of Pastoral Care at United Regional Health Care System in Witchita Falls, Texas. Susan is a popular writer for LifeWay and formerly helped coordinate Fall Festivals of Marriage and other events. She and her husband have three children.

BEFORE YOU BEGIN

Dr. Gary and Barb want to make this study, *The 5 Sex Needs of Men and Women*, a good experience for you personally and for your marriage.

Hearing about the topic of sex in a Christian marriage may be uncomfortable at times. Talking about this topic, even with your spouse, may be even more uncomfortable. Let's reassure you from the outset (as you will hear in the first session!)—making a commitment not to embarrass your spouse is important in every aspect of marriage. Certainly, we would not violate that commitment in this marriage study.

Believe it or not, you're more likely to accept the challenges offered to grow personally and to strengthen your marriage if you do so **in the presence of other committed couples**. Your church may be offering this study and you plan to be a part of the group. If so, sign up and be faithful members. You may have picked out this study on your own. Then, enlist your own group of two or three other couples. The title will intrigue them, and the focus on sexuality will draw them into the study ... just like it did you!

Begin the study by transferring session times directly into calendars, blackberries, PDFs, and refrigerator schedules. **Protect the time**.

The first seven sessions discuss the five sex needs of men and women, with each one getting focused attention and practical interpretation. The rest of the study is much more meaningful if you've done the work of the first seven sessions. Certainly, the entire 12-week study will provide so much more benefit than attending hit-or-miss.

In the viewer/discussion guide, each session has several pages. They are designed to guide your experience as you watch Dr. Gary and Barb teach on the DVD that you have purchased along with this viewer guide. You may have purchased a box set of three sessions or you may have the 12-DVD set. Use the session number to watch the corresponding DVD title.

While you watch these videos, take notes in your guide, and discuss your thoughts with your spouse and (hopefully) with your study group. In these 12 sessions, you will be considering several key biblical truths:

- God created sex; it's His idea.
- God created men and women, and He created them to be different from one another ... on purpose!
- Great sex in a godly marriage is God's plan for marriage, designed to bring us pleasure and deep joy

If you want these truths to be your marriage truths, you will need a team of three—you, your spouse, and God. Together, you'll make a powerful team that can produce a healthy marriage.

Here are the elements you'll find in each session:

- **Biblical Foundation**—a key Scripture for the session. Why not memorize that Scripture by taking turns saying it to your spouse several times during the week?
- **Good Beginnings**—a warm-up activity to help your group members connect to each other and to some key idea in the teaching to come.
- **Coaches' Comments**—a listening guide for the video to help you capture Dr. Gary and Barb's teaching as your marriage coaches and to remember key concepts. Read through it quickly before the DVD plays so that you are listening for the information the guide seeks to preserve.
- **TTYM** or Turn to Your Mate—a point in each session where our coaches prompt you to begin a discussion with your spouse. Often, you'll finish these discussions later in the session or even after a session concludes.
- **Shared Wisdom**—additional discussion questions to process with your spouse or group after the DVD portion. Consider rotating the leadership of each session among the couples in the group. Occasionally a few basic supplies need to be provided. You'll find the mate-

rial quite user-friendly; in fact, a facilitating couple has only a few responsibilities: start on time, turn on the DVD, keep the group moving through the session and its activities, guide or prompt discussion, and watch the clock. (Somebody out there is paying a baby-sitter!)

- **PoP**—Expect God to pop something into every session designed for your personal needs and then treasure it. (You don't have to share if you don't want to.) By writing them in your viewer guide or on separate paper (journal? legal pad?), you won't lose those PoPs. You will want to return to them in following weeks.

  Your PoPs may come through a Scripture, a spoken prayer, during the video teaching, in a conversation with your mate, or your group's comments. These are merely the vehicles that will prompt the Holy Spirit's reflections in the quiet of your heart.
- **Date Your Mate**—a commitment that Dr. Gary and Barb will ask you to make in Sessions 2-12. You'll find these suggestions useful to continue the conversation you and your spouse have already started.
- **Good Endings**—a suggestion for prayer time as you close the session.

The Great Marriage Experience Video Series

This 12-session DVD and viewer guide is based on the Rosbergs' book, *The 5 Sex Needs of Men and Women.* You may choose to use the book as a complement to this viewer guide to reinforce what you are learning.

The Great Marriage Experience is part of the Rosbergs' nationwide campaign to keep marriages alive and well. The Rosbergs' teaching comes from research, years of counseling couples, from conference-leading and book-writing; it comes from the accumulation of their experiences as a married couple and as marriage coaches impacting couples worldwide.

They have proven that much of marriage joy comes from the intimate connection that sex makes possible; we also know that much personal and relational heartache comes from the misunderstandings and missteps about sex. The longer we are married, the more convinced we are that a healthy sexual relationship in marriage will produce a healthy marriage. **It's that important**.

That's why you'll hear from the outset that this study does not coach you on "technique or position"; rather, it focuses on your *position* in Christ—who you are and were created to be, and the teachings of Scripture—to show us how godly people act in a marriage designed by God.

We hope *that* excites you about participating in *The 5 Sex Needs of Men and Women!* To get the most from the study, you will need:

- A copy of this viewer guide, one per person;
- A journal to write in (legal pad, looseleaf paper, what works for you);
- *The 5 Sex Needs of Men and Women* videos that provide the teaching for each session;
- Enough courage to admit—by showing up for the study!—that you love your spouse and care deeply about your marriage;
- Enough faith to believe that God can work in your life through this study to mature you personally, to enliven your marriage relationally, to make your marriage a model for your children and grandchildren, and to offer the witness of a godly marriage to your church and community;
- Enough humility to admit, in prayer, that you need God's grace and guidance for your marriage;
- Enough longing to hear Him say of your marriage, designed by Him, "And it is very good." (See Genesis 1:31.)

 You're ready to begin! Enjoy this 12-session, purpose-filled journey with your spouse and with other couples ... for the joy of your marriage and to the glory of God!

REDEFINING SEX

BIBLICAL FOUNDATION

"Marriage should be honored by all,
and the marriage bed kept pure" (Hebrews 13:4).

GOOD BEGINNINGS

Begin the session by reading the **Biblical Foundation**.
Pray for participants in this study and their willingness
to strive for an even better marriage.

If you and your spouse are meeting with other couples,
introduce yourself to the group. Tell how long you have been married.
Total the number of years of marriage represented.

Since our Scripture for session 1 mentions
the "marriage bed," recall with each other or get
with another couple to describe the first bed you had
as a married couple (and possibly the source of it!).
What was your bedroom décor?

COACHES' COMMENTS

"You can have _____ sex in a _____
marriage."

Survey says!

#2 need for men is _____ _____.

#2 need for women is _____, which means to women

talk and emotional _____.

Redefining sex:

1. We cheat when we withhold our _____ from our mate.

2. We cheat when we withhold _____ from our mate.

3. We cheat when we withhold _____ from our mate.

4. We cheat when we are _____.

Is it ever OK to say no?

You are God's provision for your mate's _____

_____.

Satan will tempt you because of lack of _____-_____.

God's plan involves:
- H _____
- L _____
- R _____
- C _____

Key conclusions:

Marriage needs an environment of healthy _____.

It is important to understand our _____.

TTYM
"What are some of your top sex needs?"

"Jot down what you think are some
of your mate's top sex needs."

SHARED WISDOM

1. Turn to your mate and take each other's pulse! Everyone still breathing?

2. Tell each other your ending to this sentence: "Now that the first video is finished, I feel _____."

3. Answer individually: I really like (choose one or more)
   - ○ the subject matter
   - ○ the group
   - ○ the place we are meeting
   - ○ the video coaches
   - ○ the workbook
   - ○ the idea of dating my mate

4. One person volunteer to read aloud the **Biblical Foundation** from the Amplified Version, printed below:

   "Let marriage be held in honor (esteemed worthy, precious, of great price, and especially dear) in all things. And thus let the marriage bed be undefiled (kept undishonored)" (Hebrews 13:4, AMP).

5. Review Pete's story, told by Barb during the video, and the four statements she made about how we sometimes cheat our mates. If God's way is other-centered, what is the center of the average marriage?

6. Write *T* (true) or *F* (false).
   1. ____ God is important in our marriage.
   2. ____ We never talk about God *and* sex in the same conversation.
   3. ____ We don't understand what God has to do with sex.
   4. ____ We are very aware of God's role in our sexual relationship.

7. Pray this prayer silently as you read. "Dear God, I praise you because I am loved by you and created for a purpose that you planned, a purpose that included my marriage to (your spouse's name). Give me the grace never to embarrass my precious mate and the desire to be other-centered in my marriage, following the example of Christ who came to save and to serve. In His name, and for my marriage's sake, I pray. Amen."

PoP

Take three minutes on your own to jot your thoughts:

1. On a scale of 1-10, with 10 being the highest, how much do you agree with the **Biblical Foundation** verse? _____

2. If your response number were one higher (even if you wrote 10), what is one thing you would be doing now?

3. What one thing did you hear that convinces you to invest yourself in this study for the benefit of your marriage?

DATE YOUR MATE

Dr. Gary and Barb will guide you in these special moments beginning in session 2.

GOOD ENDINGS

Pray for each other and for the impact of this study on your marriage.

WHAT SPOUSES NEED

BIBLICAL FOUNDATION

"Encourage one another and build each other up
as you are already doing" (1 Thessalonians 5:11, HCSB).

GOOD BEGINNINGS

Begin by reading the **Biblical Foundation**.
Pray that God will give us open ears and hearts to His message today.
Tell each other your favorite way to be encouraged.

If you are studying in a group, assign one person to each of the
10 sex needs (1-5 for women; 1-5 for men). Each person should
take notes on his or her assigned need during the video
and share comments with the group after the video is over.

COACHES' COMMENTS

Understanding intimacy

Men invite _____ through _____.

Women invite_____through emotional _____.

Barb's suggestions

1. _____ each other.

2. Differences are _____ _____.

1 Thessalonians 5:11 teaches:

1. "_____ one another."

2. We are putting each other _____ _____

   if we aren't meeting each other's _____.

Top 5 Sex Needs in Marriage

	Women	Men
#1	_____	_____
#2	_____	_____
#3	_____	_____
#4	_____	_____
#5	_____	_____

Three things to do in this study:

1. Check your _____ _____
   to your spouse and to your marriage.

2. Plan a _____ _____
   to talk to your spouse.

3. _____ give your sex life to _____.

TTYM

"If you would want me to meet one of the sex needs
this week, which one would you want it to be?"

"How can I serve you in meeting your sex needs?"

SHARED WISDOM

The Rosbergs conclude this session with three suggestions they want participants to do during this study. The first is to "check your commitment level to your spouse and to your marriage."

1. Offer ideas that describe commitment either to marriage or to a spouse. As ideas are shared, discuss: *How does commitment correspond with the top 5 sex needs mentioned on the video?*

2. Recall the one central theme in this video: *The goal is the same. Both want intimacy!* Read the following dictionary definitions of intimacy[1].
   a. the state of being intimate
   b. a close, familiar, and usually affectionate ... relationship
   c. an amorously familiar act
   d. sexual intercourse
   e. privacy, esp. as suitable to the telling of a secret

3. Notice that "sexual intercourse" is only one of the definitions. Discuss the implications of that being only a part of an intimate relationship, especially in light of the sex needs given by the Rosbergs.

4. The video discussion also taught "intimacy is a holy place before God." Read the following Scriptures which describe our relationship with God: Exodus 33:13; 1 Chronicles 28:9; John 1:18; Acts 22:14; Ephesians 1:17; Philippians 3:8,10-11; Colossians 1:6; 2:2. What did you learn from these passages?

5. Discuss how we develop an intimate relationship with God. Then discuss the similarities in developing intimacy in marriage.

6. Read this poetic statement of intimacy: "the absence of fences created a mysterious intimacy in which no one knew privacy."[2]

   What part of my life do I keep fenced off from my mate?

   Do I value my privacy more than our intimacy?

PoP

Take three minutes on your own to jot your thoughts.

1. On a scale of 1-10, how much does the **Biblical Foundation** verse describe your actions and words regarding your spouse this past week? _____

2. If that number were one higher (even if you wrote "10"), what would you be doing differently than you are now?

3. What one thing did you learn about intimacy that will benefit your marriage?

---

1. intimacy. Dictionary.com. *Dictionary.com Unabridged (v 1.1)*. Random House, Inc. *http://dictionary.reference.com/browse/intimacy* (accessed: May 15, 2007).
2. intimacy. Dictionary.com. *WordNet® 3.0*. Princeton University. *http://dictionary.reference.com/browse/intimacy* (accessed: May 15, 2007).

DATE YOUR MATE

In this DVD, the Rosbergs urged, "Be students of one another." "Study" your mate this week, recording positive thoughts about him or her in a journal. Before your next session, schedule 30 minutes in a favorite place you enjoy. Bring your journals and share your answers.

GOOD ENDINGS

The third assignment is to "prayerfully give your sex life to God." End this session by turning to your mate and praying aloud for each other, asking God to help you remember to attend to each other's needs and requesting that He bless your marriage.

MUTUAL SATISFACTION & AFFIRMATION

BIBLICAL FOUNDATION

"The husband should fulfill his wife's sexual needs, and the wife should fulfill her husband's needs. The wife gives authority over her body to her husband, and the husband gives authority over his body to his wife" (1 Corinthians 7:3-4, NLT).

GOOD BEGINNINGS

Begin by reading the **Biblical Foundation** and pray, thanking God that His creativity is so evident in His design of men, women, and marriage.

Bring a stack of note cards with you and write as many uses as you can think of for 99 pennies, one idea per card. Be creative! If you're in a group, collect all the cards, shuffle them, read them one at a time, and pick the top three most creative uses. In the video session, you will learn one more creative use for 99 pennies.

COACHES' COMMENTS

Getting Started

What works _____ the bedroom works

_____ the bedroom as well.

#1 Need for Wives: _____

Affirmation shows she is still _____ in her

_____'s eyes.

Problem: Women compare themselves to other _____.

Men _____ with other men.

____ % of women list affirmation as their #1 need.

#1 Need for Husbands: _____ _____

____ % of men list mutual satisfaction as their #1 need.

_____% of men's _____ - _____
is locked up in this area of sexuality.

Tips to wives:

Affirm outside the bedroom: Bless a _____
decision and a strong stand.

Affirmation inside the bedroom: Remind him of what he does

_____.

Ideas for affirmation (jot down suggestions from video and
any you may have):

TTYM

Husband: "What can I do to affirm you
inside and outside the bedroom?"

Wife: "What can I do to ensure our sexual
relationship is mutually satisfying?"

SHARED WISDOM

1. Read Luke 10:27 and Romans 13:8 out loud. Remember that the video suggested thinking of your spouse as your closest neighbor or "neighbor-spouse." Reread the two Scriptures above, inserting "neighbor-spouse" as you read. In your opinion, how does "neighbor-spouse" change the meaning of the verses?

2. Offer some verbal affirmation of what your spouse does well, something that reveals his/her personality to you, and a special way he/she shows you love.

3. List benefits of noticing and affirming what is good, right, and best.

4. If you are in a group, form two groups and give these assignments. **Wives,** discuss the statement from the video, "Women will compare themselves to other women," in light of these Scriptures: Galatians 6:4; Philippians 3:8; and Romans 5:15-17. Be prepared to tell the men's group your insights into the statement and the teaching of Scripture. **Husbands,** discuss the statement from the video, "Men compete with other men," in light of these Scriptures: 1 Corinthians 9:24-25 and 2 Timothy 2:4-5. Be prepared to tell the women's group your insights into the statement and the teaching of Scripture.

   After reports from each group, consider this insight: both men and women are in a battle with pride and a false sense of worth. These attitudes don't benefit marriage—ever!

5. Remind each other of the teaching Gary led, exhorting men to "bounce your eyes;" in other words, not to allow a look to linger when something or someone attractive vies for your attention. One Christian evangelist said about this topic, "It's the second look that will get you." Discuss in general terms how society's suggestive, explicit sexual messages can hinder your commitment to your spouse and keep you from focusing on what is right about him or her.

PoP

Take three minutes on your own to jot your thoughts:

1. On a scale of 1-10, indicate the degree to which you have treated your spouse as your "neighbor-spouse" this past week? _____

2. If that number were one higher (even if you wrote "10"), what would you be doing differently than you are now?

3. What one thing did you learn about practicing affirmation that will benefit your marriage?

DATE YOUR MATE

Plan a 30-minute date sometime during this week.
Bring each other a gift of what you believe to be
your spouse's favorite drink and snack.
Affirm your spouse if she or he is right;
let them know if they missed the mark!
Reflect some more on the TTYM questions.

GOOD ENDINGS

Ask God for courage to keep your focus on
loving Him and loving your neighbor-spouse.

SESSION FOUR

CONNECTION

BIBLICAL FOUNDATION

"Among the Lord's people, women are not independent of men, and men are not independent of women" (1 Corinthians 11:11, NLT).

GOOD BEGINNINGS

Begin by reading the **Biblical Foundation** verse. Pray, thanking God that He wants to connect with us and has provided a way.

Bring examples of "connectors" to spread on a table such as tape, Legos®, pipe couplings, puzzle pieces, electrical splices, and so on. Talk informally about your thoughts on connection: why it is needed, the importance of the extra piece that keeps two other pieces joined together, the negative association of disconnects, and other ideas.

COACHES' COMMENTS

Regarding wives:

____ % of women list this as their second need—for their husbands

to connect to their _____.

When a woman's connection need is not met, she:

1. Becomes _____, upset, and disappointed.

2. Becomes _____ and resentful of her husband.

3. Pulls away from her husband _____.

Regarding husbands:

_____ connection with your wife.

Tip to husbands: In the first _____ minutes you reunite, establish a

_____ _____, a _____
for the rest of the evening.

Connection must be done _____!

_____ times a week, write in your planner, "How can I _____
around the house?"

Take _____ during the day about what

to _____ her.

Regarding "bidding":

Bidding is what? Capture all the descriptive words Gary uses.

Husbands become _____ when bidding is ignored.

Since men are only allowed to express _____, that
is how they respond in these instances.

Your husband's heart is _____ up after sexual
connection.

TTYM

"Tell each other about a time you felt really connected."

Ask: "What can we do to connect that way again?"

SHARED WISDOM

1. Have you ever felt lonely in your marriage? O no O yes O occasionally
   Marriage is meant for the sharing of life and love. Why, then, might we
   feel isolated?

2. Read this journal entry about loneliness: "The loneliness was so bad
   tonight that it sucked all the oxygen out of the room. It was so intense
   it felt like it could peel the paint off the walls."[1]

   Think of other images of what loneliness feels like. Jot a few down
   here.

3. How does meaningful connection, described in this session's DVD,
   help dispel the loneliness in marriage?

4. If you are studying in a group, do the connections you are forming
   session by session with other couples help or hinder your connection
   to your husband/wife? Why or why not?

5. Spend 10 minutes in two groups, one for wives and one for husbands.
   Discuss the issue of anger as it was presented in the video. Include
   the following Scriptures from Proverbs about anger: Proverbs 12:16;
   14:29; 15:1,18; 16:32; 19:11; 22:24; 27:4; 29:8,11,22.

6. Gather again as one group. Pool your wisdom on the topic of anger
   and how it negatively impacts the connection between husband
   and wife. Together read out loud Psalms 86:15: "But you, O Lord,
   are a God of compassion and mercy, slow to get angry and filled
   with unfailing love and faithfulness" (NLT).

   How does the character of God help us with our own anger?

PoP

Take three minutes on your own to jot your thoughts:

1. On a scale of 1-10, indicate the degree to which you have connected meaningfully with your spouse this past week. _____

2. If that number were one higher (even if you wrote "10"), what would you be doing differently than you are now?

3. What one thing did you learn about connecting with your spouse that will benefit your marriage?

---

1. Tim Hansel, *Through the Wilderness of Loneliness* (Elgin, IL: David C. Cook Publishing, 1991), 23.

DATE YOUR MATE

This week, try the Rosbergs' prescription for a "great marriage"—
20 minutes a day set aside to be together. Alternate deciding
where and when you will spend these 20 minutes. At the end
of each day's date, write in this workbook one thing that was
a benefit to you both, one thing on which you both agree.

GOOD ENDINGS

Compose a prayer to God, confessing your need of Him
to manage your anger, to heal feelings of loneliness, and to
meaningfully connect to your mate ... all for His glory. Consider
sharing your prayer with your mate before the next session.

RESPONSIVENESS & NONSEXUAL TOUCH

BIBLICAL FOUNDATION

"Love cares more for others than for self. Love doesn't want what it doesn't have" (1 Corinthians 13:4, The Message).

GOOD BEGINNINGS

Begin by reading the **Biblical Foundation**. Pray for this opportunity to learn even more about our spouses and a godly marriage.

Begin this session passing around the wedding albums! Allow time to look through each other's wedding day photos. Then, give each couple one minute to tell the best and the worst moment of their wedding. If you are not in a group, take a few minutes to leaf through your album just with your spouse.

COACHES' COMMENTS

#3 Need for Wives: _____ _____

Definition: Expressing _____ and _____

as an end in itself; it does not lead to _____.

The sexual relationship is not _____, _____, _____,

but _____, _____, _____.

#3 Need for Husbands: _____

When he initiates, he takes a _____. If she doesn't respond,

he feels _____ and _____.

Why women say no:

1. Sex is not on her _____.

2. Because of her _____ of things to do.

3. Because she may not feel you _____ her.

Battle Plan!

1. Wives, say _____ as often as you can.

2. Be clear on why you say _____; this gives your husband respect

   and says the expectation will be _____ later.

3. Take the _____ % challenge—say _____ 10% more of the time.

4. Never engage in sex if it leads to _____.

5. Husbands, communicate "I _____ you more than I care

   about _____."

TTYM

Husbands, ask:
"What types of nonsexual touch do you like?"
Wives, ask:
"How can I respond better to your sexual needs?"

SHARED WISDOM

1. Individually review your notes in the **Coaches' Comments.**
   Make the following notations in the margins:

   Write "ouch!" beside the statement that was most difficult to hear.
   Write "wow!" by the statement that gives you help in relating well.
   Write "thank you!" by the statement that increases your understanding.

2. Remember that asking for what you want in marriage and getting
   what you want from your spouse requires a mutual, deep commitment
   to love like God loves. Read 1 Corinthians 13:4-7 from *The Message*
   or a similar translation, taking turns reading one line each until all
   the passage has been heard.

   Take time to make the same notations of "ouch!" "wow!" and "thank
   you!" as you did in step 1. As you are willing, share your notations.

3. Compare the verses of 1 Corinthians 13 with the additional Scripture
   to the right.

1 Corinthians 13:4	1 Thessalonians 5:14
1 Corinthians 13:4	Numbers 25:13; Galatians 4:17
1 Corinthians 13:4	1 Corinthians 4:6
1 Corinthians 13:5	Mark 10:45; Philippians 2:4
1 Corinthians 13:5	Acts 17:16
1 Corinthians 13:6	Psalms 119:142; John 8:14; 14:6
1 Corinthians 13:7	James 1:12

4. In your journal, write a love letter to your mate finishing these
   sentences:
   What I've learned about your #3 sexual need, specifically that …
   I've been reminded of how godly, scriptural love behaves, such as …
   I commit to show you love in ways taught in Scripture, like …
   When I stumble in showing you my love and meeting your needs,
   help me by saying and doing things such as …

5. Without revealing what has been written, share how you felt writing
   this letter. What do you think the benefits will be?

PoP

Take three minutes on your own to jot your thoughts:

1. On a scale of 1-10, indicate the degree to which you relate to your spouse with a 1 Corinthians 13 kind of love. _____

2. If that number were one higher (even if you wrote "10"), what would you be doing differently than you are now?

3. At what point in this session did you feel the material was tailor-made for you? Record that insight. How will it benefit your marriage?

DATE YOUR MATE

After this session, exchange journals with your spouse to read the love letter written during the session. Plan the time and place for this exchange so that you will be uninterrupted, your conversation will be private, and your connection to each other unhindered.

GOOD ENDINGS

Don't forget your wedding albums when you leave!

Spend time as a couple interceding to God for your fears and asking Him to draw you closer through the exchange of letters.

SESSION SIX

INITIATION & SPIRITUAL INTIMACY

BIBLICAL FOUNDATION

"When two or three of you are together because of me,
you can be sure that I'll be there" (Matthew 18:20, The Message).

GOOD BEGINNINGS

Begin by reading the **Biblical Foundation.**
Pray for healing and new openness with your spouse.

Write on paper this phrase: "I would like it if you would ..." and finish
the phrase with ordinary household chores such as mow the lawn,
empty the dishwasher, pick up the kids, and so on. As you read each
chore, your spouse may choose any one of three responses:

1. That would be my pleasure.
2. I'm a little bit hesitant about that.
3. That is outside the boundaries.

COACHES' COMMENTS

Getting started:

Spiritual intimacy makes the ordinary _____.

We all have a _____ in our hearts.

Tips to husbands:

1. _____ your wife to Jesus.

2. Begin to _____ up about your needs.

3. Pray _____ your wife. Any woman wants her husband

   to be her greatest _____ in prayer.

4. Pray _____ your wife.

5. Pray for God to bless your marriage bed.

   Spiritual intimacy is _____ people pursuing a _____

   relationship with Christ, overflowing into a _____

   relationship in marriage.

A wife's plan for initiation:

1. Remember that your husband is a _____ being.

2. So are you as his wife! View yourself as a _____

   _____.

3. Refuse to buy into the _____ about sex.

4. Keep _____ the sex in your marriage.

5. Your husband wants to feel _____, _____,

   and _____.

TTYM

For husbands:
Take your wife's hands and initiate prayer with her.

After that prayer, wives ask:
"What can I initiate with you sexually?"

SHARED WISDOM

1. Reconstruct the story the Rosbergs told from a caller to their radio program, the dilemma of a woman married to a nonbeliever, and what happened at church.

   What feelings were stirred in you as you heard this story?

   Describe the difference between "praying for" and "preying on."

2. Barb talks about the "hole in my heart," a hole that all of us recognize. List some of the ways people try to fill in that hole.

3. Read out loud together the following verses from Psalms 68:

   "Blessed be the Lord, Who bears our burdens and carries us day by day, even the God Who is our salvation! Selah [pause, and calmly think of that]! God is to us a God of deliverances and salvation; and to God the Lord belongs escape from death [setting us free]" (vv. 19-20, AMP).

   Then clasp hands and each pray silently for God to carry your spouse's burdens and needs.

4. If you are in a group, husbands review "Tips to husbands" and wives review "a wife's plan for initiation." Share any insights from your marriage that relate to the content your group discusses.

5. Personally assess the impact of this course to you at this point. You've just crossed the halfway mark! Write in your journal and then share with your spouse or group your thoughts about one or two of these statements:

   "The most significant truth I've learned ..."
   "The Scripture that has been most meaningful ..."
   "The way I have grown in my personal life as a husband or wife ..."
   "The personal growth I want to affirm in my spouse ..."
   "The benefit to my marriage so far ..."

PoP

Take three minutes on your own to jot your thoughts:

1. On a scale of 1-10, with 10 being extraordinary, how far has your marriage moved from ordinary toward extraordinary? _____

2. If that number were one higher (even if you wrote "10"), what would you be doing differently than you are now?

3. What one thing did you learn about the myths about sex that will benefit your marriage?

DATE YOUR MATE

Use this date time to try out the communication exercise the Rosbergs described. Take turns saying, "I would like it if you would ..." and finish the statement. Remember all that you learned in session 5 about how love acts and talks, and be guided by those Scriptural truths as you complete this exercise.

GOOD ENDINGS

Conclude by praying out loud for each other, expressing gratitude for specific choices, behaviors, and words of your spouse.

AFFIRMATION & ROMANCE

BIBLICAL FOUNDATION

"You have stolen my heart, my sister, my bride; you have stolen my heart with one glance of your eyes" (Song of Songs 4:9).

GOOD BEGINNINGS

Read the **Biblical Foundation** and thank God that He is the origin of love.

Make a valentine that conveys one reason why you love your spouse. As a couple, exchange valentines.

COACHES' COMMENTS

Learning from Valentine's Day

Men equate foreplay with _____, and romance with

_____.

Treat her as if _____ _____ is Valentine's Day.

Crossing the beautiful bridge

Love is a _____. Romance is a daily _____.

The Angry-Free Zone

1. Write it on _____.

2. Put it on the _____.

3. Get a clean _____.

4. My mate is not my _____.

   Remember, my enemy is _____.

5. _____ with your mate that you don't want the enemy

   to have anything to do with your _____.

Love and Respect

Note how romance is connected to the husband's need for

_____.

Given a choice between love or respect from their wives,

husbands choose _____.

A wife's words have _____ over the heart of her husband.

A husband needs his wife to "_____ _____" into his life
to show respect for him.

_____ _____ against any other voices that you let
into your life. Remember the warnings of Proverbs about the sound
of another voice.

TTYM

For husbands:
"What are some things I can do to romance you?"

For wives: Tell your husband two
or three things you admire about him.

SHARED WISDOM

1. Begin working individually on the third question in the PoP exercise on page 37.

2. As couples, reveal the answer you wrote and explain why.

3. If you are in a group, attach a list of your answers—one for husbands and one for wives—on a focal wall. Affirm the other groups' answers.

4. At your house what would be the opposite of affirmation (circle one):

   silence   being taken for granted   perfectionism
        criticism   poking fun

5. Offer a prayer to God consisting only of affirmations of who He is and what He does.

6. Review the notes you've taken about the "Angry-Free Zone." Brainstorm answers to these two questions:
   a. Why is anger so powerful?

   b. What is the relationship between anger and fear?

7. Brainstorm ways anger becomes evident in a marriage, both active (shouting, throwing things, making threats) and passive anger (not speaking, withholding emotions). Be bold enough to offer examples of your own behavior (do not speak for your spouse).

8. Turn to your mate and confess these things:
   "When I am angry, I am more (active or passive) in showing it."
   "I know that I have hurt you and weakened our marriage when I... (give two examples of anger behavior from either list)."

9. As you hear these statements from your spouse, resist the urge to minimize what was said or to respond with something like, "Don't worry about it." Instead, make this response: "The next time you are angry enough to act in those ways, what do you need from me?"

PoP

Take three minutes on your own to jot your thoughts:

1. On a scale of 1-10 (with 10 being the highest), how carefully do you guard your marriage relationship from anything that would damage it?

   _____

2. If that number were one higher (even if you wrote "10"), what would you be doing differently than you are now?

3. (For wives)
   Write one thing you learned about affirming your husband.

   (For husbands)
   Write one thing you learned about romancing your wife.

DATE YOUR MATE

Base your date on Lamentations 3:22-24. Plan your date for first thing in the morning. Go out to breakfast together; sit outside with your favorite morning beverage; plan a walk or hike ... and simply speak in love and act lovingly toward each other. Remember to affirm God's faithfulness to provide fresh mercy every morning.

GOOD ENDINGS

Pray, affirming your love for God and desire to please Him in your marriage.

ELEPHANTS
IN THE BEDROOM

BIBLICAL FOUNDATION

"Do not conform any longer to the pattern of this world,
but be transformed by the renewing of your mind.
Then you will be able to test and approve what God's will is—
his good, pleasing and perfect will" (Romans 12:2).

GOOD BEGINNINGS

Begin by reading the **Biblical Foundation** and
praying for God's will to be known to us.

Complete this statement: "The only thing more preposterous
than having an elephant in the bedroom is having _____
in the bedroom ... which we do!" (In other words, tell
one example of the odd or interesting thing that is
currently in your bedroom, such as what's under the bed!)

COACHES' COMMENTS

What Elephant?

Reasons we don't talk:

1. Because of _____

2. Because it doesn't feel _____

3. Because we grew up in homes where it's _____ to talk
   about it

4. By not talking about it, we assume it's _____ or _____ is connected to it.

The Impact of Pornography

"I used to have to chase after my sin; now my sin is chasing after me."

Put the temptation into the _____.

Proverbs 4:23 warns, "Above all else, _____ your heart, for it is the _____ of life." Everything emanates from the heart.

Whittle the Elephant Down to Size

1. Follow a "no" with "_____."

2. Respect your mate's _____ _____.

3. Let your test turn to _____.

4. Don't talk about sex in the _____.
   Choose a time when there's safety and security.

5. Pay attention to the more _____ spouse.

6. Don't expect your spouse to be a _____ _____.

7. Get the _____ _____ out of the bedroom!

TTYM

"What is your best memory of our sexual history?"

"What most encouraged you?"

SHARED WISDOM

1. The Rosbergs teach that a change of mind is required to change your words and actions. Look at the list of suggestions to "Whittle the Elephant Down to Size." Talk about the change of mind needed to follow these suggestions. For example, "Let your test turn to testimony" requires you to be open before God and your spouse about the difficult times in your marriage relationship.

2. To add to your discussion take another look at the **Biblical Foundation** for this session from the Amplified version below:

   "Do not be conformed to this world (this age), [fashioned after and adapted to its external, superficial customs], but be transformed (changed) by the [entire] renewal of your mind [by its new ideals and its new attitude], so that you may prove [for yourselves] what is the good and acceptable and perfect will of God, even the thing which is good and acceptable and perfect [in His sight for you]" (Romans 12:2, AMP).

3. Review "The Impact of Pornography" in **Coaches' Comments.** Gary's suggestion is to put your temptation into the light. Examine these Scriptures about light: John 8:12; 11:9-10; 2 Corinthians 4:6-7. What insights do you gain from these truths about changing

   your mind?

   your words?

   your actions?

4. Take turns reading aloud the following Scripture references: Psalm 18:28; 19:8; 27:1; 36:9; 43:3; 56:13; 89:15; 97:11. Then choose the Scripture about light that is most meaningful to you and offer a reason for that choice.

PoP

Take three minutes on your own to jot your thoughts:

1. On a scale of 1-10, how frequently do you see evidence of God's "good, pleasing and perfect will" in your marriage? _____

2. If that number went one higher (even if you wrote "10"), what would you be doing differently than you are now?

3. What personal application do you need to make of this statement from the video: "I used to have to chase after my sin; now my sin is chasing after me"?

DATE YOUR MATE

The statement at the conclusion of the video was this:
"Let's put into the light what the enemy desires to keep in the dark."
So the date this week, again following the Rosbergs' advice,
is to plan a time for sexual intimacy with a light on in the room.

GOOD ENDINGS

Pray, dedicating yourself to be God's light to others around you.

WHEN LIBIDOS DON'T MATCH

BIBLICAL FOUNDATION

"Do nothing out of selfish ambition or vain conceit,
but in humility consider others better than yourselves.
Each of you should look not only to your own interests,
but also to the interests of others" (Philippians 2:3-4).

GOOD BEGINNINGS

Begin with reading the **Biblical Foundation.**
Pray that each couple will find ways they complement each other.

COACHES' COMMENTS

God's Plan Includes Our Differences

If you've been married for any length of time, you've experienced

_____ libidos.

Things that may lower libido:

1. _____ imbalances. Our bodies are like a delicate snowflake.

2. Depression. ____% of us will go through depression.

3. _____ that depress the sex drive and make you feel lethargic

4. Unrelenting _____ leading to depression or burnout

5. _____

Then Comes the Baby Carriage!

1. Get some _____; share your roles together.

2. Get away with your _____.

3. Keep your marriage a _____. The greatest gift you can give your children is to love their dad, or to love their mother.

4. Let your husband know you're _____ to a healthy sexual life.

5. Take marriage _____.

How To Get in the Mood When You're Not

1. _____. Ask God: "Is there something I can do? What is it you want to teach me?"

2. Share your _____.

   ____% of sex is in our minds.
   Challenge what we say in our minds, our underlying assumptions.

3. Pay attention to your sexual _____.

4. Remember _____ _____ that worked. When you've taken care of all other issues, think back to those special times.

5. Just do it. Step into the _____.

6. _____.

TTYM

"How often would you desire to make love in our marriage?"

"What is blocking the frequency of sex in our marriage?"

SHARED WISDOM

1. Discuss the **Biblical Foundation** Scripture, Phillipians 2:3-4, and then Psalm 139:13-14. How have you tried to keep these two ideas balanced in your marriage?

2. Each couple needs two quarter-sized circles of paper. Write the word *me* on one paper and *you* on the other. Then attach them to the two sides of a quarter. Keep this coin in your bedroom to remind you of the balance always needed between your uniqueness and your obligation to other-centeredness. Pray for each other.

3. Gary and Barb discussed many things about different ages and stages of life that affect libido. Share ideas that were particularly helpful to you at your stage of life.

4. Barb listed several marriage vitamins to rekindle your sex life: daily kisses and hugs, flirting, how you play with each other, getting your mate's attention. Jot down at least five more suggested "vitamins" to this list. You will need them later, during your date.

5. In you are in a group, form a team for the wives and one for the husbands. Discuss suggestions from the section "How To Get in the Mood When You're Not" by sharing the one suggestion that:
   I find most helpful to me
   I'm resisting ... and here's why
   I need your prayers for me

6. Reflect together on how your marriage is being strengthened after nine sessions in this study. Affirm each other's growth, and encourage your mates to volunteer areas where they continue to struggle or have yet to see change.

7. Offer each other a closing benediction by reading together Psalm 139:23-24.

PoP

Take three minutes on your own to jot your thoughts:

1. On a scale of 1-10, how well does Philippians 2:3-4 describe your attitude about your sexual relationship with your spouse? _____

2. If that number were one higher (even if you wrote "10"), what would you be doing differently than you are now?

3. Choose one of the six suggestions given above for "How to get in the Mood When You're Not," and write in your journal your plan for making good use of that suggestion.

DATE YOUR MATE

In this session, you considered "marriage vitamins" that can rekindle your sex life. During your date find an interesting container for your collection of marriage vitamins. Fill it with these and other suggestions until you have 31 in your container. Take turns choosing one each night for a month. Encourage and affirm each other's suggestions.

GOOD ENDINGS

Pray that God will give you the physical
and spiritual strength you need
to have an even better marriage.

WHEN YOU'RE TOO EXHAUSTED FOR SEX

BIBLICAL FOUNDATION

"In six days the LORD made the heavens, the earth, the sea,
and everything in them; but on the seventh day he rested.
That is why the LORD blessed the Sabbath day and set it apart as holy"
(Exodus 20:11, NLT).

GOOD BEGINNINGS

Begin by reading the **Biblical Foundation.**
Pray that God will show us His priorities for our lives.

Describe what seemed to you to be the longest day of your life.

COACHES' COMMENTS

Redbook reported: _____ million American women are too tired
or exhausted for sex.

Making Sex a Priority

Exhaustion is one area we can have control over.

1. _____.

2. Work _____.

3. Say _____ to some things tempting you to say _____.

4. Decide where you must _____.

Things That Must Change

1. _____ changes

2. Ask ourselves _____ we do _____ we do.

3. Learn to _____ _____ so that you have something to give to your marriage and family.

4. _____ yourself.

More Practical Suggestions

1. Learn the boundaries between work and home.

2. Schedule sex for a _____ until it becomes a _____.

3. Put some _____ back in your week.

4. Plan a _____ at least once a year.

5. Turn off the _____.

6. _____ up.

TTYM

"What is it that makes you too tired to have sex?"

"What is one step you will take?"

SHARED WISDOM

1. Discuss Dennis Rainey's image of a scale, with work on one side and marriage on the other. On a blank piece of paper put into a sentence the truth you've heard. Post your sentence on a focal wall.

2. Identify what is getting your best right now.

3. List three things that replenish you.
   a.

   b.

   c.

4. Choose one of the five "More Practical Suggestions" given above, and discuss your plan for making good use of that suggestion.

5. Take a few minutes to have everyone read the extra information on "Boundaries" on page 58. Discuss which concepts in the article you found important and how couples can implement these key ideas in their marriage.

6. What do you lose when you don't "boundary up" your life and your marriage?

   What does your spouse lose when you don't "boundary up" your life and your marriage?

   What does your marriage lose when you don't "boundary up" your life and your marriage?

PoP

Take three minutes on your own to jot your thoughts:

1. On a scale of 1-10, how tired are you?

1	2	3	4	5	6	7	8	9	10
NOT TIRED				TIRED				VERY TIRED	

2. What number would represent a balanced, rested life to you? _____
   Explain why.

3. What one thing could you be doing differently than you are now
   to achieve that number?

DATE YOUR MATE

Set aside 10 minutes a day for the next week to read out loud
to each other. Choose a book that has to do with better life
management, stress reduction, or another marriage-building topic.
Make notations in the margins of the book as you read it. Be prepared
to share what book you chose at your next group meeting.

GOOD ENDINGS

Pray for each other as you look for just the right book.

FUN AND EXCITEMENT
IN THE BEDROOM

BIBLICAL FOUNDATION

"Kiss me and kiss me again, for your love is sweeter than wine"
(Song of Songs 1:2, NLT).

GOOD BEGINNINGS

Begin by reading the **Biblical Foundation**. Kiss your spouse!

Review this list of popular love songs. At another time use these titles—
or others you know—to think of a plan for expressing your love for
your spouse such as a short story or poem, a montage, a scrapbook
page, or printed lyrics on beautiful paper. Check the instructions
at the end of this session to know more about your assignment.

Fly Me to the Moon	I Wanna Hold Your Hand	Love Me Tender
Happy Together	Endless Love	You Light Up My Life
I'll Be There	In Your Eyes	I'll Stand By You
I Want to Know What Love Is	I Say a Little Prayer for You	I Think I Love You
It Must Have Been Love	Melt With You	Woman in Love
Unforgettable	Total Eclipse of the Heart	Forever and Always

COACHES' COMMENTS

1. Begin with the **Biblical Foundation** of Song of Songs 1:2:

   Kiss _____ and with _____.

2. Bask in the _____ of sex.

3. Practice good _____. Be wonderful close up!

4. Create the _____ for sex. Spruce up the bedroom.

5. Recall Song of Songs 4:16. Become a student of your spouse's

   sexual _____.

6. The "O" word—_____.

7. Understand and appreciate sexual _____.

   Invite God to _____ your heart with what

   first _____ your heart about your mate.

8. Understand the different kinds of sex:

   _____ _____

   _____ sex: when we need to meet the other's need

   _____ sex: when there's been hurt, loss, or betrayal

   _____ sex: extensive amounts of time behind
                              locked doors

9. Cordon off the _____ and _____
   for passionate sex.

10. Have the mindset of "_____ _____?"

TTYM

Discuss a time when you made love and
it was exciting. "What made it so fun?"
"What can we do to insure that our
next time together is just as exciting?"

SHARED WISDOM

1. For each couple: Read the instructions silently. Then on a blank piece of paper complete the assignment.

   - Title the paper "Our Home Improvement Blueprints."
   - Draw the outline of the doors, windows, and walls in your bedroom.
   - Now sketch in the major pieces of furniture.
   - Indicate some of the other prominent features that probably don't add to a romantic mood (a stack of old newspapers or magazines, the unfolded laundry in the laundry basket, the treadmill, and so on).
   - Inspired by the #4 suggestion from the Rosbergs, "spruce up the environment," agree together to list five ways you will make your bedroom more beneficial to sexual intimacy.

2. If you are in a group, listen to one or more ideas from this list. You may choose to put together a combined list of all suggestions.

3. Remember that doing small, practical, unromantic things such as "no more dust bunnies sharing our space!" can produce romantic results.

4. Volunteer to read aloud these two Scriptures that use the phrase "wife of your youth"—Malachi 2:14-15 and Proverbs 5:18 (NIV). Discuss what connection they have with "fun and excitement in the bedroom." Acknowledge the incredible freedom that comes to your spouse when he or she knows you are unconditionally committed to him or her until death.

5. From the 10 suggestions given by the Rosbergs (see **Coaches' Comments**), tell your favorite one, adding your own idea as to how to make this suggestion work.

6. Husband: Read aloud Song of Songs 4:1-7 to your wife.
   Wife: Read aloud Song of Songs 5:10-16 to your husband.

   Conclude with a 10-second kiss.

PoP

Take three minutes on your own to jot your thoughts:

1. On a scale of 1-10, how much does your marriage resemble the romantic joy expressed in the **Biblical Foundation** Scripture? _____

2. If that number were one higher (even if you wrote "10"), what would you be doing differently than you are now?

3. In **Shared Wisdom** you selected your favorite from the 10 suggestions in the **Coaches' Comments** for creating more fun and excitement in your bedroom. Choose another one or more, and write your plan for making good use of that suggestion.

DATE YOUR MATE

Follow this session with a group date—yes, just what your parents always wanted! Choose a place where your group has the freedom to be noisy. Bring the gift you started at the beginning of this session. One couple at a time, present your gift, and then accept the cheers of your group and the gratitude of your spouse.

GOOD ENDINGS

Close with prayer that we will want our Christian lives to be as exciting and adventurous as we are planning for our sexual lives. Ask God to be number one in our marriages.

GOD IN THE BEDROOM

BIBLICAL FOUNDATION

"I am convinced that nothing can ever separate us from God's love. Neither death nor life, neither angels nor demons, neither our fears for today nor our worries about tomorrow—not even the powers of hell can separate us from God's love ... nothing in all creation will ever be able to separate us from the love of God that is revealed in Christ Jesus our Lord" (Romans 8:38-39, NLT).

GOOD BEGINNINGS

Begin by reading the **Biblical Foundation** and thanking God for His presence and love.

If you are in a group, exhange addresses with the other couples. Write notes to each other, thanking each other for this shared experience.

COACHES' COMMENTS

God is much _____ than an owner's manual.

Focus on being ____._____-_____.

Inviting God into the bedroom acknowledges that God's way _____!

• When we go God's way, we're going to experience all the joy; this

keys _____, _____, and _____ out of the marriage bed.

A Relationship of Three

We can't trust one another apart from _____.

We trust the work that _____ is doing.

Confession ... Again

Many times with breakdowns and blocks in intimacy, there is

_____ _____. You can't root it out apart from

the _____ of _____.

You may be saying, "We can't reclaim the ground Satan has stolen."

Remember the promise, "_____ can separate us from the love of Christ" (Romans 8:38-39).

Final Advice

1. _____ _____ the ground!

2. "God, your _____ is good enough for me."

3. If you are _____, remember God _____.

4. God wants to be in the _____ of your bedrooms and of your lives.

5. _____ the temptation to say "Yeah, but ..." or "If you would only ... ."

TTYM

"Do we know the Creator of the sexual
aspect of our lives?"

"Do we want to know Him better?"
Read the ABCs of Salvation on page 59.

SHARED WISDOM

1. Share key insights that you will never forget from the entire 12-session experience.

2. If you are in a group, save time for anyone who has never publicly told the story of how God became "the real deal" in his or her life. Certainly affirm and encourage anyone willing to do this.

3. Review the notes in "A Relationship of Three." Compile a prayer list that any couple could use to more effectively and more fervently pray for each other and for their marriages.

4. It could be that one of God's purposes in this study for you was to strengthen your marriage so that you are secure enough to share your strength with others. Would you be open to facilitating a group for another Rosberg study? Give careful thought to that possibility. How might that happen?

5. The meaning of "good-bye" derives from an older saying of the phrase "God be with you." If you are in a group, telling each other good-bye after this journey you've taken together is not a casual thing, and offering a blessing as you depart is evidence of how important this experience has been.

6. Form groups of two or more couples. Have couples take turns telling the other couple(s):

    • the growth you've seen in their relationship;

    • what you have learned from them in this group;

    • how their marriage has blessed your marriage;

    • what you'll always remember about them.

    Follow this time of affirmation by praying for one another in these small groups.

PoP

Take three minutes on your own to jot your thoughts.

1. On a scale of 1-10, how much does your life reflect your experience of God's forgiveness and everlasting love? _____

2. If that number went one higher (even if you wrote "10"), what would be different in your daily life than it is now?

3. Does your spouse already know your answers to the first question?
   ○ yes ○ no

   What does he or she not know about your relationship with God that you are now willing to share?

DATE YOUR MATE

First, agree on a regular date that you two will continue.
Second, plan a celebration date for completing this study, one that both of you will enjoy. Talk more on this date about "what's next?" in your commitment to your marriage and to others' marriages. Consider planning a reunion date with your study group for six months from now.

GOOD ENDINGS

Express your prayer in a different way by singing one of the many worship songs about God's love.

BOUNDARIES

What they are and what they do

A boundary ... [is] a metaphor for the "line" that delineates what is oneself from what is not oneself. The concept of a boundary can also be used to define what a relationship is from what it is not. Just as every self should have a clearly established and communicated boundary line, so should every relationship. ... Proper boundaries promote several key essentials of healthy relationships:

Responsibility: Once it is established what is "me" and what is "not me," I know to assume ownership of, and responsibility for, what is "me."

Freedom: Boundaries set the stage for personal freedom, both of oneself and of one's partner in relationship. With clearly delineated boundaries, I will not be continually frustrated attempting to "fix" matters on someone else's property, but will attend to what I do have control over, namely, myself. ...

Love: The exercise of self-control over one's own property ... Boundaries are especially crucial in marriage—which is, after all, primarily a relationship of love. Without boundaries, love falters, and marriage fails... "Boundaries relinquish other-control for self-control (Galatians 5:23)."

Protection: When the other person in a relationship dishonors your personal boundaries—and/or those of the relationship—then your boundaries can serve to protect you from injury. This is accomplished by taking control of your own territory and securing its perimeter against harmful intrusions, rather than by taking control of the one who would hurt you. ... The net result of such action usually is to limit what the other can get away with in his relationship with you. But you do not prevent the other from engaging in bad behavior; he remains free to do so if he chooses. The price for such behavior is simply shifted from you to the one who is responsible for it.

Accepting Reality: When we establish and communicate boundaries in relationships, we say "no" to elements of abuse, control, manipulation, and denial in those relationships ... [We choose not to] remain enmeshed in an illusory and self-destructive quest to "win" the love of someone who simply does not have it to give.

1. Rebecca Merrill Groothuis, "Evaluating the 'Boundaries' Therapy of Cloud and Townsend," *Denver Journal: An Online Review of Current Biblical and Theological Studies,* no. 3 (2000), *http://www.denverse-*

THE ABCs OF SALVATION

Some people think a personal relationship with God is something only theologians can comprehend. Actually, God's plan of salvation is simple enough for everyone to understand. Here are the ABCs of salvation.

ADMIT

Admit to God that you are a sinner. All persons need salvation. Each of us has a problem the Bible calls sin. Sin is a refusal to acknowledge God's authority over our lives. Everyone who does not live a life of perfect obedience to the Lord is guilty of sin. "For all have sinned and fall short of the glory of God" (Romans 3:23, HCSB). Since none of us is perfect, all of us are sinners (Romans 3:10-18).

The result of sin is spiritual death (Romans 6:23). Spiritual death means eternal separation from God. By God's perfect standard we are guilty of sin and therefore subject to the punishment for sin, which is separation from God. Admitting that you are a sinner and separated from God is the first step of repentance, which is turning from sin and self and turning toward God.

BELIEVE

Believe in Jesus Christ as God's Son and receive Jesus' gift of forgiveness from sin. God loves each of us. God offers us salvation. Although we have done nothing to deserve His love and salvation, God wants to save us. In the death of Jesus on the cross, God provided salvation for all who would repent of their sins and believe in Jesus. "For God loved the world in this way: He gave His one and only Son, so that everyone who believes in Him will not perish but have eternal life" (John 3:16, HCSB).

CONFESS

Confess to others your faith in Jesus Christ as Savior and Lord. After you have received Jesus Christ into your life, share your decision with another person. Tell your pastor or a Christian friend about your decision. Following Christ's example, ask for baptism by immersion in your local church as a public expression of your faith. "If you confess with your mouth, 'Jesus is Lord,' and believe in your heart that God raised Him from the dead, you will be saved. With the heart one believes, resulting in righteousness, and with the mouth one confesses, resulting in salvation" (Romans 10:9-10, HCSB).

ANSWER KEY

Session 1: great, godly; sexual intimacy; intimacy, connection; heart; attention; affection; selfish; sexual needs; self-control; honor; love; respect; cherishing; communication; differences.

Session 2: intimacy, sex; intimacy, connection; compliment; God's design; encourage; at risk, needs; 1. affirmation/mutual satisfaction; 2. connection/connection; 3. nonsexual touch/responsiveness; 4. spiritual intimacy/initiation; 5. romance/affirmation; commitment level; date night; prayerfully, God.

Session 3: inside, outside; affirmation; great, husband; women; compete; mutual satisfaction; 67; 90; self-image; courageous; right.

Session 4: 59; heart; grouchy; irritable; sexually; schedule; 15, tender heart, connection; daily; 3, help; notes, tell; frustrated; anger; opened.

Session 5: nonsexual touch; love, affection, sex; me, me, me, we, we, we; responsiveness; risk, frustrated, emasculated; radar; list; respect; yes; no, met; 10, yes; embitterment; love, sex.

Session 6: extraordinary; hole; escort; open; for, advocate; with; two, vertical, horizontal; sexual; sexual being; myths; vibrant; needed, special, cherished.

Session 7: romance, sex; every day; feeling, action; paper; table; start; enemy, Satan; agree, heart; affirmation; respect; power; speak belief; guard yourself.

Session 8: conflict; natural, taboo; dirty, shame; light; guard, wellspring; when; danger zone; testimony; bedroom; timid; mind reader; snow tires.

Session 9: mismatched; hormones; 20; medications; stress; aging; rest; mate; priority; committed; vitamins; pray; attitude; 80; desires; past experiences; intimacy; exercise.

Session 10: 24; reprioritize; less; no, yes; succeed; behavioral; why, what; hold back; replenish; season, pattern; Sabbath; gateway; television; boundary.

Session 11: deeply, passion; afterglow; hygiene; environment; zones; oneness; peaks; surprise, captured; quick interlude; functional; comfort; passionate; time, energy; why not.

Session 12: bigger; other-centered; works; strife, anger, control; Christ, God; unconfessed sin, Spirit, God; nothing; take back; grace; discouraged, is not done with you yet; midst; resist.

DO YOU WANT TO EXPERIENCE A GREAT MARRIAGE?

DO YOU WANT OTHERS IN YOUR CHURCH TO EXPERIENCE A GREAT MARRIAGE?

The Great Marriage Experience is a dramatically different approach to discovering a **Love That's Real** and **Love That Lasts.** Dr. Gary & Barb Rosberg provide The Great Marriage Experience for couples, churches, and other groups committed to building godly marriages.

LOVE THAT'S REAL

The Great Marriage Experience begins with a **comprehensive look** at your marriage through an online marital assessment. It continues with periodic events, catalytic to the growth of your marriage. These **real-life tools** help you know where you marriage is today, where you want it to be in the future, and how to get there. Experiencing a great marriage means it is distinctly biblical, a godly love, a real love.

LOVE THAT LASTS

The Great Marriage Experience also provides **ongoing marriage coaching and encouragement** in a variety of ways **over time.** The Rosbergs' nationally syndicated radio program offers a **daily dose** of coaching and encouragement in your marriage. Dr. Gary & Barb also offer a unique **monthly** partnership program called Coaches Club that delivers marriage coaching, dating ideas, and encouragement directly to you on **relevant topics** in your marriage. Used **periodically** throughout The Great Marriage Experience, books, CDs, and DVDs from the Rosbergs provide **biblical insight and in-depth coaching.** The Great Marriage Experience equips you to enjoy a convenant marriage—that truly lasts a lifetime.

**To learn more about
The Great Marriage Experience visit**
www.TheGreatMarriageExperience.com
or call (888) 608-COACH

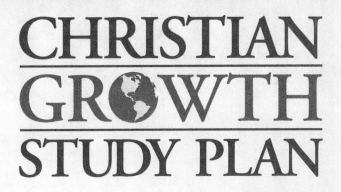

CHRISTIAN GROWTH STUDY PLAN

In the **Christian Growth Study Plan,** *The 5 Sex Needs of Men and Women* is a resource for course credit in the subject area Personal Life of the Christian Growth category of plans. To receive credit, read the book, complete the learning activities, show your work to your pastor, staff member or church leader, then complete the following information. This page may be duplicated. Send the completed page to:

Christian Growth Study Plan; One LifeWay Plaza; Nashville, TN 37234-0117; FAX: (615)251-5067; E-mail: *cgspnet@lifeway.com*

For information about the Christian Growth Study Plan, refer to the Christian Growth Study Plan Catalog online at *www.lifeway.com/cgsp.* If you do not have access to the Internet, contact the Christian Growth Study Plan office at (800) 968-5519 for the specific plan you need for your ministry.

THE 5 SEX NEEDS OF MEN AND WOMEN
CG-1317

PARTICIPANT INFORMATION

Social Security Number (USA ONLY-optional) | Personal CGSP Number* | Date of Birth (MONTH, DAY, YEAR)

Name (First, Middle, Last) | Home Phone

Address (Street, Route, or P.O. Box) | City, State, or Province | Zip/Postal Code

Email Address for CGSP use

Please check appropriate box: ❑ Resource purchased by church ❑ Resource purchased by self ❑ Other

CHURCH INFORMATION

Church Name

Address (Street, Route, or P.O. Box) | City, State, or Province | Zip/Postal Code

CHANGE REQUEST ONLY

❑ Former Name

❑ Former Address | City, State, or Province | Zip/Postal Code

❑ Former Church | City, State, or Province | Zip/Postal Code

Signature of Pastor, Conference Leader, or Other Church Leader | Date

*New participants are requested but not required to give SS# and date of birth. Existing participants, please give CGSP# when using SS# for the first time. Thereafter, only one ID# is required. **Mail to:** Christian Growth Study Plan, One LifeWay Plaza, Nashville, TN 37234-0117. Fax: (615)251-5067.

Revised 4-05